The Crocs go to the shop to get a tub.

Pam grins. She is thinking of
a thin, red tub with lots of froth.

Tim thinks that is not much fun.
He is thinking of a big, fun
tub with lots of things in it!

Sam is thinking of a tub of mud.

Pip thinks of a black tub
with pink things.

Then they spot a big, big tub.

This tub is thin and red, big
and fun ...

... with lots of mud and lots of pink things! Rub-a-dub-dub!

Spelling and writing

Cover the words below. Say the first word (*thing*). Ask the child to repeat the word and tap out the phonemes in order with his or her fingers, saying each phoneme (*th-i-ng*) and then writing the graphemes to spell the word. Repeat this with the other words.

thing

much

shop

Understanding the story Ask the questions below to make sure that the children understand the story.

1 Who wants a thin, red tub? (page 2)

2 Which tub does Sam want? (page 4)

3 Which bath do the Crocs get? (pages 9 and 10)

Assessment

Say the phonemes

Point to each grapheme in turn and ask the child to say the corresponding phoneme. Note whether the child is correct each time and go back to any incorrect ones.

Next, cover the graphemes. Say a phoneme and ask the child to write the corresponding grapheme. Prompt the child to write /z/ in two different ways. Practise any that are incorrect.

th	z	ng	y
ch	sh	qu	zz

Read the words

Ask the child to sound out a word and then blend the phonemes and say the word. Repeat this with the other words.

ship   chip   bang   froth